Forestry Commission
Handbook 7

Treeshelters

By M.J. Potter
Formerly Silviculturist,
Forestry Commission

LONDON: HMSO

ISBN 0 11 710288 1

ODC 236.3: (410)

Keywords: Establishment, Arboriculture, Forestry

British Library Cataloguing in Publication Data
A CIP catalogue record for this book is available from the
British Library

HMSO publications are available from:

HMSO Publications Centre
(Mail and telephone orders only)
PO Box 276, London, SW8 5DT
Telephone orders 071-873 9090
General enquiries 071-873 0011
(queuing system in operation for both numbers)

HMSO Bookshops
49 High Holborn, London WC1V 6HB 071-873 0011 (counter
service only)
258 Broad Street, Birmingham, B1 2HE 021-643 3740
Southey House, 33 Wine Street, Bristol, BS1 2BQ (0272)
264306
9-21 Princess Street, Manchester, M60 8AS 061-834 7201
80 Chichester Street, Belfast, BT1 4JY (0232) 238451
71 Lothian Road, Edinburgh, EH3 9AZ 031-228 4181

HMSO's Accredited Agents
(see Yellow Pages)

and through good booksellers

Acknowledgements

I must, first and foremost, express appreciation of
Graham Tuley's innovatory role in initiating the treeshelter
project and undertaking the first 4 years of development.
Graham tells me that he was ably assisted in this task by a
considerable force of Silviculture (South) foresters, but in
particular Phil Risby.

Additionally, I should like to thank Graham Tuley,
Gary Kerr, Harry Pepper, James Lang Brown, Karl Lee,
Richard Jinks, Gail Taylor, Donald Thompson, Julian Evans
and David Burdekin for comments on and contributions to
the text.

Gratitude is also owed to Roger Boswell, Tracy Houston
and Ralph Coates who have been responsible for
overseeing design and undertaking the statistical analysis
of a large number of diverse treeshelter experiments.

Editor's note

This Handbook was written by Mark Potter during his
employment with the Forestry Commission's Research
Division. He has since taken up employment with a
commercial producer of treeshelters.

Front Cover   3-year-old oak in treeshelter with 1 metre
diameter weed control by herbicide application. *(39660)*

Inset   This Douglas fir 4 years after planting illustrates
that most conifers also derive benefit from treeshelters.
(39163)

Contents

Preface

A frustration often experienced by researchers is the time lag between the publication of experiment results and incorporation of the findings into current practice. A notable exception to this state of affairs occurred with the introduction of treeshelters when demand for the new technique outpaced the rate at which research results could be collected.

It is rare for silvicultural traditions to be disturbed so abruptly and the speed of change in accepted broadleaved practice inevitably provoked a reaction among many wishing to defend familiar methods. Conversely, some foresters, seeing an answer to all the difficulties they faced, adopted the new idea with abandon and extended the use of treeshelters into inappropriate applications or on an uneconomic scale.

This Handbook attempts to give clear guidance on the use of treeshelters along with a balanced appraisal of their benefits and limitations. The topics covered are separated into those relating to the design of treeshelters, the benefits that may be anticipated, and correct usage. A brief description of the microclimate inside treeshelters is given in an appendix at the end of the Handbook.

Treeshelters

Summary

Treeshelters are translucent plastic tubes up to 2 metres in height that are used to protect young trees, while modifying the microclimate in ways that improve survival and enhance growth rates. This Handbook describes the development of treeshelters over the first 10 years of their use and summarises the features required in a successful shelter. It describes the environment inside a shelter and reports the response of trees to these conditions. It also intends to give a balanced view of the benefits and disadvantages of treeshelters and examines the limits of their applicability.

ABRIS POUR LES ARBRES

Résumé

Les abris serres sont des tubes plastiques translucides d'une hauteur pouvant atteindre 2 m. Ils améliorent la survie el la croissance des jeunes plants puisqu'ils les protègent du gibier et créent un microclimat. Ce manuel décrit les différentes étapes de developpement de ce type d'abris depuis son introduction en 1980 à nos jours, et résume les caractéristiques essentielles d'un abri efficace. Il explique les mécanismes qui modifient l'environnement à l'intérieur d'un tube, et la réaction des jeunes plants à ces nouvelles conditions. Nous espérons, en examinant aussi les limites d'utilisation de ce type d'abris, donner une vue objective des avantages et inconvénients d'un abri serre.

SCHUTZHÜLLEN FÜR BÄUME

Zusammenfassung

Schutzhüllen sind durchscheinede bis 2 m hohe Kunststofffröhren, die junge Bäume schützen, indem sie das Mikroklima abändern, und sowohl Überleben als auch Wachstum verbessern. Dieses Handbuch beschreibt die Entwicklung von Baumschutzhüllen während der ersten 10 Jahre ihrer Verwendung, und fasst die in einer erfolgreichen Schutzhülle erwünschten Eigenschaften zusammen. Das Handbuch beschreibt auch die Umwelt in einer Schutzhülle, und berichtet die Reaktion des Baumes auf diese Verhältnisse. Die Absicht ist auch, die Vor- und Nachteile von Baumschutzhüllen objecktiv darzustellen, und die Grenzen ihrer Anwendbarkeit zu untersuchen.

Introduction

Treeshelters offer a convenient solution to many of the problems faced during the establishment of trees in Britain. These include the difficulty of weed control, severe animal damage and the risk of prolonged drought following planting. In the lowlands a further consideration is the small scale of operations which often means that fencing and cultivation are prohibitively expensive.

The development of treeshelters began in 1979 when Graham Tuley wrapped polythene sleeves around plastic mesh guards to create a 'mini-greenhouse' effect around individual trees. Since then treeshelters have often been referred to as 'Tuley tubes', as well as 'grow-tubes', 'tree-tubes', and a number of other epithets, some of which are now registered trade names. Usage in this Handbook is confined to the terms 'treeshelter' and 'shelter'. It should be noted that 'tree guard' is not a suitable synonym as this refers to a physical barrier around each tree, usually made from plastic or wire mesh, used specifically to protect small trees from damage by animals and machines.

Since their inception treeshelters have been used in over 200 Forestry Commission experiments on sites throughout Britain. The results from this work have provided the detailed information reported here and upon which treeshelter design and practice have been based.

In 1979, 180 treeshelters were made by hand for use in the first experiment and in the following year about 1750 shelters were used on research sites. By 1984 the

WHAT IS A TREESHELTER?

There are a number of ways of providing protection for individual young trees, resulting in occasional confusion of terminology and applications. It is useful to differentiate between treeshelters and other devices.

Treeshelters are transparent or translucent tubes that create a 'mini-greenhouse' environment around single trees while offering protection from mammal damage. Shelters are attached to stakes and should provide support and protection for between 5 and 10 years after planting before the material begins to break down.

Tree guards, made from metal or plastic mesh, are intended primarily to provide protection from mammal damage. They have very little further effect on the environment around the growing tree and do not constrain side branches or leading shoots. These may grow through the mesh which can become embedded in the growing stem.

PLATE 1 Sessile oak emerging from treeshelters two growing seasons after planting. Note the weed-free area. *(38057)*

9

use of treeshelters was an accepted forest practice and the number sold in Britain was well over a million. Current annual production probably exceeds 10 million. At the moment it is difficult to foresee the level at which the market will reach saturation. It was initially predicted that the maximum annual use could be as high as 15 million, but it is conceivable that this figure could be exceeded as the planting of small pockets of broadleaves increases and shelters are used more widely in medium-scale forest planting such as is occurring in response to the Farm Woodlands Scheme. As use in Britain continues to expand, several overseas countries have also adopted treeshelters with enthusiasm. It now seems possible that most temperate forest industries will eventually find a role for this method of establishment.

The reasons for the rapid acceptance of the tree-shelter are evident: correctly used, shelters can reduce the losses caused by mammals, the cost of herbicide application, the time spent on inspection and maintenance, and the stresses associated with the transfer from nursery to planting site. Despite the relatively high initial investment, treeshelters can in fact lead to cost savings by avoiding the need for fencing, enabling herbicide applications to be made more efficiently and improving survival.

Although the possible benefits from treeshelters are considerable they should not be used without an awareness of their limitations. Large areas will usually be established more cost-effectively if protection from animals is provided by means of fencing. When shelters are used on sites with a high density of deer, supplementary protection may be required to prevent fraying if the treeshelters break down before the trees are about 10 years old.

The size of shelter selected should be no taller than that required to offer protection from those animals known to pose a risk: on sites with little evidence of deer the protection offered from a 600 mm shelter will be sufficient. If there is no threat from animals it may be difficult to justify expenditure on shelters in terms of improved growth and survival alone.

Treeshelter design

Size

Where there is a risk of browsing, the top of the treeshelter needs to be just above the browse height of the damaging animal. This height may range from 600 mm to 2 m and is discussed in the section dealing with protection from animal damage.

Diameter is less critical. Experiments have tested designs with diameters from 50 mm upwards. In general it can be said that as diameter increases, the shelter effect declines, but within the range 50 — 200 mm this is not important. Although a 50 mm wide shelter would require less material and be easier to transport it would be very difficult to slide over plants without causing damage. For ease of use most shelters produced have diameters (or sides) between 80 and 120 mm.

Shape

The first commercially produced shelters were made from flat sheets of polypropylene folded into square tubes. This is a convenient shape to handle and is reasonably robust. However, the large flat sides of these shelters offered considerable resistance to wind and this sometimes caused the shelter to turn in the wind or blow flat against the stake. The problem was reduced by producing shelters with a hexagonal cross-section, but these models were more difficult to erect. Shelters produced by folding sheet material generally have little resistance to crushing and in many situations will be vulnerable to pressure from browsing animals.

PLATE 2 60 cm treeshelters are sufficient to provide protection from rabbits and voles on level sites. *(39159)*

11

Those treeshelters produced directly from tubular extrusion are much more difficult to crush and are less likely to be affected by gusts of wind. However, they also occupy more space for the same number of shelters. This problem has been reduced by producing a range of diameters that nest inside one another.

Material

Nearly all treeshelters available today are made from twin-wall polypropylene. This material has the advantage of relative cheapness and a good strength to weight ratio but it will deteriorate rapidly in sunlight unless stabilised with ultraviolet inhibitors. The early shelters, made without added stabiliser, began to break down at the corner folds during their first year in sunlight and disintegrated steadily thereafter. Experience has determined the formulation that will offer a 5-year field life in full light in southern Britain, enabling the treeshelter to remain intact until the tree is able to support itself.

Polypropylene is sometimes used as a single-wall material. The manufacturing process for this is cheaper, but greater quantities of plastic and stabiliser may be required to provide sufficient strength. Such designs offer less rigidity for the same weight of plastic.

Polyvinylchloride (PVC), which has the advantage of high light transmission, was tried in several early designs but was found to deteriorate too quickly. However, one current design has overcome this by incorporating a polyester matrix that holds the base material intact. This design has shown no signs of decay after 8 years and it can be expected that treeshelters made from such material will have to be cut away before they damage the tree.

PLATE 3 The shelter material should begin to degrade after a minimum of 5 years' service. *(M.J. Potter)*

PLATE 4   As the treeshelter disintegrates the litter should be gathered up for disposal.   *(37230)*

With all treeshelter designs the problem of litter should be avoided by collecting up and disposing of waste material at the end of the establishment period. Although treeshelters are generally viewed favourably as they encourage the planting of broadleaves, the proliferation of fragments of plastic in the countryside could do much to provoke opposition to their use unless a little effort during the quiet days of winter is devoted to maintaining the appearance of young plantations.

14

Stakes

Attempts to produce free-standing treeshelters have not been successful and all current designs depend on a stake for support. The stake may be made from wood, metal or plastic, depending on the type of shelter and intended use.

Wood is the most commonly-used material and, for most practical purposes, the most suitable. Sawn soft-wood is readily available and should be treated with preservative for use in ground contact. The length of stake required will depend on the type of shelter being used: it should penetrate the ground to a depth of at least 30 cm and project about 10 cm above the upper tie or wire, but remaining *below* the rim of the shelter. On reasonably sheltered sites with deep soil, a 25 mm × 25 mm cross-section may be adequate for a 1.2 m shelter, but if exposure to strong winds is expected or the soil contains a high proportion of stones or tree roots this specification should be increased to 30 mm × 30 mm or greater. Cleft chestnut is a cost-effective alternative and requires no preservative provided the heartwood content is sufficient. It is easily obtained in the south-east, but is less common elsewhere.

Stakes are most easily put into the ground using a small drivall, but a club hammer or mallet used with care will suffice. On stony ground it is often helpful if a small crowbar is used to start the hole.

The importance of ensuring that all stakes are squarely upright should not be underestimated: a collection of leaning shelters gives an impression of dereliction while increasing the risk of damage to the young tree.

Metal rods can be quick and easy to erect on stone-free soils but offer little frictional resistance to a treeshelter turned by the wind and may be toppled by moderate gusts. Their use should be restricted to very sheltered areas and firm soils on sites where the

PLATE 5   Stakes should be of sufficient size to support the shelter securely, but may damage the tree if they project above the top of the shelter.   *(M.J. Potter)*

PLATE 6   If treeshelters are made from non-rigid material it is important to increase the stake specification.   *(37229)*

manager can be absolutely confident that all rods will be removed before they begin to damage trees. It should be borne in mind that steel rods oxidise rapidly in ground contact and often cannot be pulled out of the ground manually after a year or more.

A number of plastic stakes of various designs have recently become available but at this stage they have not been tested fully. However, it is already evident that those made from round plastic suffer from much of the same lack of rotational rigidity as round metal.

PLATE 7 Speed of installation has been greatly improved since the introduction of pre-inserted ties. *(39160)*

Ease of installation

The first production designs used internal stakes and wire loops inserted through the shelter walls. Fixing the shelter to the stake was a difficult process and often trapped the leading shoot. Subsequent shelter designs were secured by means of a short length of wire wrapped firstly around the treeshelter and then around the supporting stake. This method of installation has proved time-consuming, unreliable and leaves a strand of wire that may become embedded in the growing stem. It is important that the means of fixing the shelter does not enclose the young tree and most currently available shelters meet this requirement by using wire ties attached to one wall, or plastic ratchet clips ('cable clips') which are quick and easy to secure.

The fixing device should also be easy to undo so that trees can be inspected and losses replaced. This is straightforward when wire ties have been used, but those types of plastic clip that are most easily undone are barely strong enough for this application. Modifications to the basic design allowing it to be released with the thumbnail are probably the best compromise.

With all these methods, care should be taken to ensure that the plant leader is not trapped by the wire or clip during installation.

Staples are sometimes used to attach the shelter to the stake. This approach has the advantage of being cheap as well as preventing the shelter from moving around the stake. However, as the shelter material decays one of the first places to fail is the area around the staple where stresses are concentrated.

Stem abrasion

Most of the materials used to make treeshelters are capable of causing damage to the stem of the emerging tree as it is moved by wind on exposed sites; the majority of shelters therefore incorporate design modifications to reduce this risk. Early attempts to alleviate this problem by the addition of a cushioning device did not prove successful and most models now rely on a flared rim to prevent stem contact with the cut edge of the plastic. The need for this adaptation should not be underestimated as young trees have been decapitated on even moderately exposed sites. Whippy species, such as ash and birch, are more prone to this form of damage than those with robust stems.

Whether or not abrasion occurs on a susceptible site is very largely determined by the position of the last set of lateral shoots to be produced before the leader emerged above the shelter rim. If the laterals are close to the top, say within 5 cm, they will act as a restriction to swaying and prevent the stem meeting the edge of the shelter with any force. Side branches lower down will offer less protection. Some species produce very pliable young shoots and foliage, and are therefore more likely to be pushed against the edge of the treeshelter.

All currently available treeshelters incorporate a design feature of some sort intended to reduce this damage. Some of these adaptations offer little improvement over the original design, while others are likely to be suitable, with appropriate species, on all but exposed sites.

Light transmission

On open sites, light-demanding species, such as ash, have grown very slightly taller in brown shelters than in white or green ones but this observation is unlikely to be of any practical importance. However, shelter colour may become relevant in underplanting or enrichment where light intensity is already low; in such cases it is advisable to choose one of the more translucent materials.

In a series of experiments designed to look at the responses of sheltered plants to different light intensities, treeshelters were made using clear PVC and polypropylene overprinted with grey and black screens with a range of opacities such that light measured at ground level inside the shelter varied from 63% down to approximately 1% of ambient. Some of the results from one of these experiments are summarised graphically in Figure 1 where it can be seen that height growth in two light-demanding species, ash and oak, continued to increase with decreasing light availability up to the treatment in which 14% of light was transmitted. With greater light interception height increment declined rapidly.

Stem diameter increment (Figure 2) began to decline at higher light intensities than height growth, suggesting that etiolation was in part responsible for maintaining height growth when more than about 55% of light was intercepted. Beech, a very shade tolerant species, showed a more or less steady reduction in terms of both growth parameters as light decreased.

Survival is, perhaps, a more important indicator of the value of treeshelters, and from Figure 3 it can be seen that the number of deaths in ash and oak was not affected by the amount of available light until the most extreme treatment, whereas beech survival declined as light interception increased.

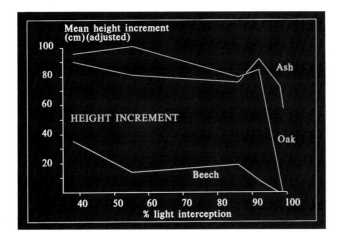

FIGURE 1   The effect of light interception by treeshelters of different opacity on the height increment of sessile oak transplants after two growing seasons.

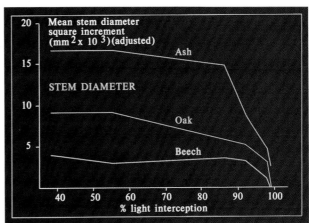

FIGURE 2   The effect of light interception by treeshelters of different opacity on the stem diameter increment of sessile oak transplants after two growing seasons.

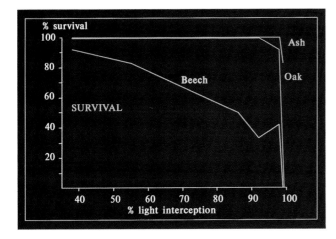

FIGURE 3   The effect of light interception by treeshelters of different opacity on the survival of sessile oak transplants after two growing seasons.

The benefits of treeshelters

Survival

When the first treeshelter experiment was established it was predicted that, although growth rates would be enhanced, mortality would be much higher than in the unsheltered treatments because of the high temperatures created in the plastic tubes. In the event, every single tree in the shelters survived while 25% of those without shelters died in the first 2 years, despite being surrounded by a deer- and rabbit-proof fence!

This pattern has been repeated on many sites under differing conditions and with a wide range of species. With a few exceptions, use of treeshelters has consistently decreased mortality during establishment. The exceptions are mostly attributable to identifiable causes, such as late frosts after flushing, late planting or poor weed control.

Reduction of outplanting stress

Dieback or plant death can be caused by low air humidity or insufficient available soil moisture during the period after planting. High temperatures and dry air both increase the rate of transpiration, which can lead to a diurnal cycle of water deficit and rehydration as plants transmit water vapour during the day and reabsorb water from the soil at night. However, if available water in the soil is scarce then the water deficit may persist, resulting in damage or death of the plant.

The problem is particularly serious when spring drought occurs immediately after planting as the young tree will not have recovered the substantial part of its fine root system that was lost as it was lifted from the nursery. Water deficit can be further exacerbated because the thinly-developed cuticle on newly-expanded leaves permits further moisture transmission from epidermal tissue. On exposed sites soil or ice particles blown by the wind can cause damage to cuticles, thus increasing passive water loss.

Inside treeshelters containing established trees the leaf-air vapour pressure difference (the 'drying power' of the air) remains relatively low once the young tree has begun to fill the space in the shelter with transpiring leaves, even during hot summer days (see Figure 11). This has the effect of slowing transpiration and passive water loss, as well as encouraging condensation on the walls of the shelter. The droplets that collect will eventually run back to the ground, again becoming available to the tree roots.

However, a newly-planted tree is less able to increase the humidity in a shelter as its transpirational capacity is lower. It is therefore possible that the effects of the high temperature will outweigh those of the only moderately increased humidity and increase the risk of water stress in a plant. This danger should be minimised by ensuring that all treeshelter planting is completed during autumn or early spring so that the young trees have the opportunity to produce an extensive root system and a quantity of transpiring leaves before hot summer temperatures are experienced. Clearly treeshelters should not be used in an attempt to extend the planting season.

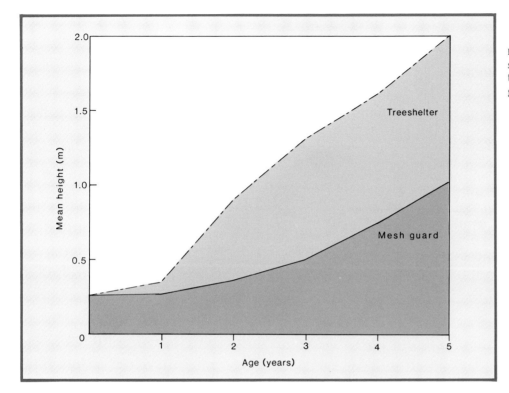

FIGURE 4 Height growth of sessile oak transplants in treeshelters and plastic mesh guards.

Wind can effect the growth of young trees in a number of ways. In some species, transpiration and the possibility of water stress are increased, with a consequently greater risk of plant death. Other species respond by reducing the rate of transpiration; over the long term this may result in reduced growth. The mechanical stresses caused by the movement of the aerial portion of a plant in wind can influence the way in which material is allocated to different parts of the growing plant. Repeated swaying leads to a thickening of the lower stem and the rapid development of a structural root system. Relieved from the action of wind movement, trees in shelters devote resources towards other activity, such as height growth.

Height growth

The most familiar effect of treeshelters is the greatly accelerated early height growth of many species. Figure 4 contrasts the height increment of oak transplants protected by treeshelters and mesh guards in an experiment near Exeter. The results presented are typical of those obtained from a large number of experiments; it can be seen that the shelters have conferred a height advantage of about 1 m, which is maintained through the early years. The size of the increase attained in other experiments has often been much greater than that shown in this example, though on some sites the height enhancement has been smaller. It is evident that the results achieved depended considerably on local conditions and plant quality.

There are few species that do not derive some benefit from treeshelters, if only in terms of the protection provided. However, it is of interest to compare the response of a range of species as those that grow most quickly will be the first to complete the establishment phase. Tables 1, 2 and 3 are based on the data collected from experiments established between 1980 and 1982 and categorise the species used into three classes according to the relative increase in height increment compared with trees protected by nylon mesh guards. It should be borne in mind that a nylon mesh guard will itself increase the height increment compared with a that of a tree with no protection or support.

It should not be concluded that treeshelters are unsuitable for use with the species listed in Table 1. In most experiments survival of the sheltered trees was greater than those without shelters, and all benefited from the protection and ease of location that treeshelters offer.

One of the reasons for an apparent poor response to shelters is that the trees in both shelter and mesh guard treatments have grown quickly. In Table 1 those species marked † exhibited a height increment in shelters of 50 cm or more after 3 years, and those with § had grown over 1 m in the same period.

Table 1   Species with mean height increment in shelters less than 50% greater than that of trees in mesh guards 3 years after planting

Common name	Systematic binomial
Horse chestnut	*Aesculus hippocastanum* †
Hornbeam	*Carpinus betulus* §
Black walnut	*Juglans nigra* †
Southern beech	*Nothofagus procera* †
Wild cherry	*Prunus avium* §
Rowan	*Sorbus aucuparia* §
Whitebeam	*Sorbus aria* †
Western hemlock	*Tsuga heterophylla* †
Western red cedar	*Thuja plicata*

PLATE 8   This Douglas fir 4 years after planting illustrates the fact that most conifers also derive benefit from treeshelters. *(39163)*

Table 2   Species with mean height increment in shelters greater than 50% but less than 100% greater than that of trees in mesh guards 3 years after planting

Common name	Systematic binomial
Grand fir	*Abies grandis*
Norway maple	*Acer platanoides*
Alder	*Alnus glutinosa*
Italian alder	*Alnus cordata*
Sweet chestnut	*Castanea sativa*
Ash	*Fraxinus excelsior*
Holly	*Ilex aquifolium*
Japanese larch	*Larix kaempferi*
Crab apple	*Malus sylvestris*
Southern beech	*Nothofagus obliqua*
Norway spruce	*Picea abies*
Sitka spruce	*Picea sitchensis*
Corsican pine	*Pinus nigra* var. *maritima*
Douglas fir	*Pseudotsuga menziesii*
Yew	*Taxus baccata*

Table 3   Species with mean height increment in shelters more than 100% greater than that of trees in mesh guards 3 years after planting

Common name	Systematic binomial
Field maple	*Acer campestre*
Sycamore	*Acer pseudoplatanus*
Birch	*Betula pendula*
Hawthorn	*Crataegus monogyna*
Beech	*Fagus sylvatica**
Common walnut	*Juglans regia*
Sessile oak	*Quercus petraea*
Pedunculate oak	*Quercus robur*
Small-leaved lime	*Tilia cordata*
Large-leaved lime	*Tilia platyphyllos*

*Beech in treeshelters

Beech was included in eight of the earliest treeshelter experiments and in all cases responded very well, with the height increment of the sheltered trees being on average 3.7 times greater than that of the controls after two growing seasons, and 1.9 times greater at the time of final assessment after 5 years. At this stage 96% of the sheltered trees were alive compared with 85% in mesh guards. In no experiment was either height increment or survival of the trees in shelters less than that of other treatments.

Since these results were first published there have been a number of reports of poor growth and survival of beech in treeshelters. On inspection it is clear that contributory factors in many of these cases are inadequate weed control or poor quality plants. Nevertheless it appears that the most likely culprit for the losses is the beech woolly aphid (*Phyllaphis fagi*). This insect is normally innocuous but can attain high populations on the beech hedges where fresh regrowth after trimming in the summer provides young leaves that are attractive to this insect. In shelters, beech exhibits a prolonged phase of growth and produces thinly-cuticularised leaves, an ideal feeding site for the aphid.

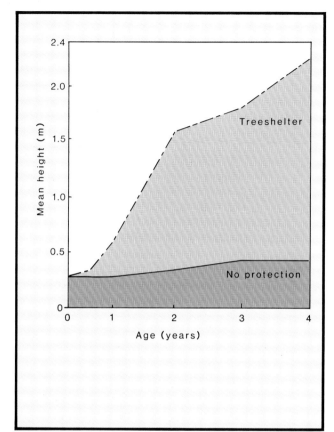

FIGURE 5 Height growth of sessile oak transplants in tree-shelters and without protection in a woodland with a moderate population of roe deer.

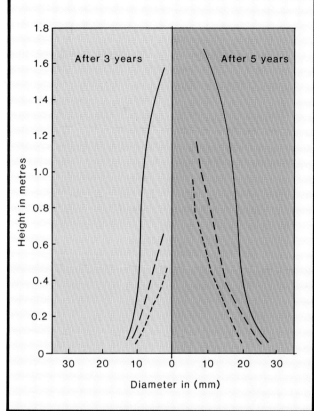

FIGURE 6 The development of stem shape of sessile oak transplants in treeshelters and without protection (after Tuley, 1985).

Although fast growth contributes to a shorter establishment period it is not the only benefit, and the use of shelters should not be precluded because the species planted does not respond well in terms of height growth. Browsing damage from deer, hares and rabbits can decimate young plantations and may result in some trees repeatedly browsed back for many years.

In such situations — and there are few sites in Britain that are free from this risk — treeshelters can offer a reliable and cost-effective means of protection. Figure 5 illustrates the growth rates of sheltered and unprotected sessile oak transplants in a woodland where a sizeable deer population is present. The effect of browsing is clear and the difference in growth rates dramatic.

Diameter growth

Although height increment is usually significantly enhanced by treeshelters, diameter growth near ground level is often not greatly changed and may be increased *or* decreased by the presence of shelters depending on site conditions and the species in question. Figure 6 illustrates the way in which stem form of the oak trees in the original treeshelter experiment changed during the course of the experiment.

At 3 years after planting the unprotected trees had developed a typical tapering stem form, whereas the stem produced within a treeshelter was virtually columnar with very little variation in diameter from a point 100 mm above ground level to the top of the shelter. After 5 years, by which time the movement of the elevated crown was probably having a pronounced effect on stem development, the stems of trees from both treatments were more similar in shape, though those originally protected by shelters were considerably taller.

It is often believed that when treeshelters decay there is a need to provide staking for the trees as the support of the shelter is lost. This belief is probably derived from the early reports from the original treeshelter experiment, in which the shelters were removed after only 3 years so that stability and branch development could be examined. At this time a proportion of the stems had not attained sufficient girth to support the crown and needed to be attached to the treeshelter stakes to keep them upright.

We now know that after 5 years most trees will have developed strong enough stems to remain erect once the support of the shelter has gone. Most currently available models are designed to have a field life of more than 5 years and to break down gradually thereafter. On sites where light levels are low and hence plant growth slower, the trees will require a

longer period to attain stability. However, the shelter material will decay at a commensurately slower rate and should continue to provide support and protection for the time needed. It can be expected that it will be a rare occurrence for additional support to be required once the shelter has broken down.

Location

A transplant may be easy to see immediately after planting but a year or two later when woody regrowth or tall weeds such as bracken, bramble or willowherb have invaded the site it can be very difficult to locate the young trees. Cutting away the competing vegetation all too frequently results in cutting the crop!

By contrast, no one can fail to find a treeshelter in even the densest vegetation and, once found, any smothering weeds can be cut away and herbicide applied with little risk to the sheltered tree. The ease of location provided by shelters reduces the need for planting in straight lines at regular spacing, which has often been partly justified by the difficulty in finding trees during the establishment period.

Herbicide application

The speed and efficiency of herbicide application around broadleaved species can be significantly increased when treeshelters are in place. There is little risk of the herbicide coming into contact with the protected trees provided a little care is taken to avoid spraying directly into the holes through which the ties or wires pass. Consequently, applications can be made when weeds are most susceptible and the user can proceed rapidly through young plantations, leading to a lower cost for the weeding operation and a reduction in the occurrence of chemical damage.

Trees are not alone in deriving enhanced growth

PLATE 9   Treeshelters enable small transplants and seedlings to be found in even the densest vegetation.   *(M.J.Potter)*

from the treeshelter environment and it is not unusual to see weeds protruding from the tops of shelters. Although this can look alarming, the competition may not be as severe as that from weeds outside the shelter provided they are not dense enough to smother the tree. Two studies looking at this problem have failed to find any correlation between the occurrence of herbaceous weeds inside shelters and the growth of the trees. Nonetheless the risk of damage will be reduced if such competition is removed and this will usually be achieved most easily by means of a root-acting herbicide such as propyzamide.

27

Protection from animal damage

The most common reason for using treeshelters is protection from animal damage. Whenever physical protection of new planting is required it is inevitably a major component of establishment costs; before undertaking this investment the forest manager should be sure that this is justified by the risk of damage. In many situations treeshelters offer a cost-effective means of achieving satisfactory protection; the relative merits of shelters and fencing are discussed later in the section on costs.

Wild animals

The earliest treeshelter experiments were sited in Alice Holt Forest where browsing by roe deer is a major establishment problem. As the browse height of roe has been determined as 1.1 m it was decided to make the first treeshelters 1.2 m tall. The extensive risk from roe deer through much of Britain means that this size has come to be seen as the standard specification, but there is no need to use a shelter this tall if deer do not pose a threat to the young trees. For instance, if rabbits are the only mammal problem then a 600 mm tall shelter will suffice, as will one 750 mm tall against hares. A 1.8 m shelter will protect from browsing by red and fallow deer but may itself be vulnerable to damage unless a substantial stake and a robust shelter design are used.

It should always be remembered that the effective height of a treeshelter will be reduced by steep slopes, uneven ground or deep snow.

Voles can cause extensive damage to young trees, particularly on grassy sites. One way of reducing this damage is to maintain a weed-free area (at least 1 m diameter) around each tree as voles are reluctant to cross bare ground. Collars that fit around the base of the tree prevent voles gaining access to the stem but as they are quite heavy they can be difficult to use on

WHAT SIZE OF TREESHELTER?

There is little point in choosing a shelter taller than that needed to provide protection from mammal damage; the faster growth rates in larger shelters will certainly not justify the extra expense. Using smaller (and hence cheaper) shelters will enable larger areas to be protected without recourse to fencing. The table below indicates the size of shelter needed to protect from a range of animals:

Rabbits	60 cm
Hares	75 cm
Roe deer	1.2 m
Sheep (small breeds)	1.2 m
Sheep (large breeds)	1.5 m
Red, sika and fallow deer	1.8 m

PLATE 10 Voles may gnaw through shelter material. *(A11011)*

small planting stock. Treeshelters offer an alternative method of protection though it is important to use a sturdy design that can be pushed a few centimetres into the soil. As voles can gain entry through a gap as small as 5 mm it is important that shelters are erected vertically and that stakes are firmly fixed in the ground to prevent tilting by animals or strong winds.

Trees in shelters may be considered to be established once they are self-supporting. In most circumstances this stage is reached 3 — 5 years after planting. At this age the trees are still vulnerable to fraying by roe deer and on some sites with a high population density it may be necessary to provide supplementary protection after the treeshelter has broken down. The time taken for the material to deteriorate will depend on the type of treeshelter used; some models may last for 10+ years by which time the trees could be past the susceptible period.

Farm stock

By adapting standard procedures, treeshelters can also be used to protect trees planted on farmland among grazing livestock.

The 1.2 m shelter will offer protection from most sheep, but it may be necessary to use a 1.5 m model where large sheep breeds are present or where ground conditions are uneven. In either case it is advisable to use a reasonably substantial stake (say 50 mm square) and a second smaller stake on the opposite side to prevent rotation of the shelter. This second stake should extend no more than 150 mm above ground level as sheep can use this as a step to reach the foliage of the emergent tree.

With appropriate measures the range of animals against which protection can be offered includes beef and dairy cattle, though, as considerable expense is inevitably involved, the costs of alternative methods should be carefully examined. Minimum require-

PLATE 11   Treeshelters can permit grazing to continue after trees have been planted.   *(38613)*

ments include a 2 m tall shelter and a stake with a top diameter of at least 70 mm. A sturdy round design should be used with a single strand of barbed wire wrapped spirally around the shelter to discourage rubbing.

It should be emphasised that treeshelters protect trees only during the establishment period, and as they disintegrate it may be necessary to provide another form of protection if grazing is to continue. If wooden guard rails are to be used to protect widely-spaced trees it is probably as well to erect these at the time of planting so that the need for them is not overlooked later.

Growth after emergence

The most familiar representation of the height growth of oak in treeshelters is the graph shown in Figure 7 which is based solely on the results from the first treeshelter experiment. A decline in height increment of the sheltered trees is seen during year 3. This has been widely interpreted as reflecting the development of a broader crown once the leader has emerged from the shelter. However, this inflexion does not occur in the data from many other experiments and is better explained in terms of the climatic damage (from both wind and frost) that was incurred on this site, not on emergence, but over a year later. Figure 4, although it reflects a less dramatic initial effect, is more typical of the growth pattern of sheltered oak transplants in most experiments, and what might be expected in normal use on most lowland sites.

Provided a species is suited to the site on which it is planted there are few reasons why crown development after emergence from a shelter should not proceed in a similar fashion to that of conventionally planted trees. In those species with weak apical dominance and considerable inherent variability, such as oak, there is a natural tendency for multiple leaders and other 'defects' to occur in a proportion of the population. Treeshelters have the effect of drawing attention to these shortcomings by raising them up to eye level.

In fact the stems emerging from the tops of tree-shelters are typically no worse than those produced without shelters. While there is an increased risk of the newly-extended shoots snapping if they are whipped by wind against the hard rim, this is adequately compensated for by the reduced tendency for oak in shelters to produce branches and the less frequent occurrence of multiple leaders. Any disorders that

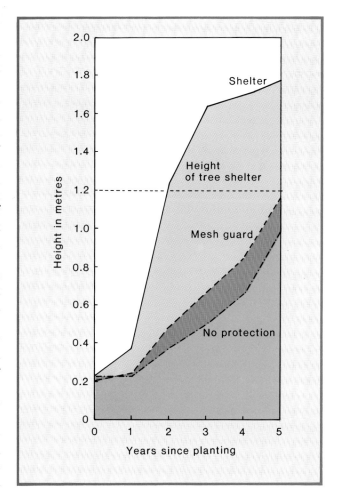

FIGURE 7   Height growth curves of sessile oak transplants from the first treeshelter experiment (after Tuley, 1985).

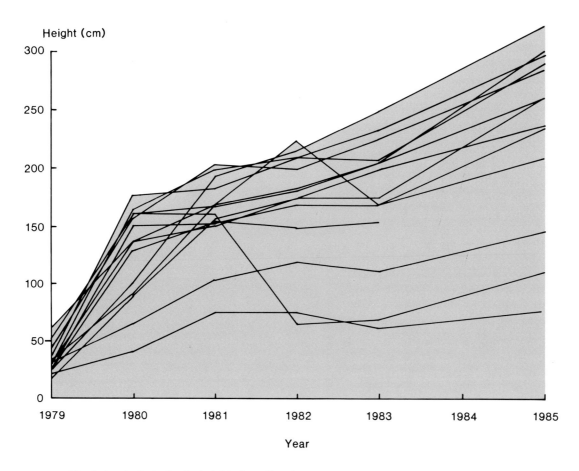

Height (cm)

FIGURE 8   Single tree trajectories for height of sessile oak
transplants in treeshelters from the first experiment.

do occur at treeshelter height are easily rectified by corrective pruning.

Figure 8 shows single tree trajectories of height versus time for a sample of the trees used in the original treeshelter experiment. It can be seen that, although the growth rates of a few trees are not greatly enhanced, the sample cannot easily be partitioned into good and bad 'responders'. The effects of the climatic damage on a few individuals in years 3 and 4 is clear. It is also evident that even those trees that appear to gain little benefit in terms of height increment are alive and growing steadily.

Correct use of treeshelters

Distribution and installation

The difficulties in handling cumbersome plastic tubes pose logistic problems for the forest manager. The system described in the box, based on work study appraisals, is suggested as an efficient means of distributing and installing treeshelters.

Maintenance

It is not sufficient to plant a tree, erect a treeshelter and abandon the site. It must again be emphasised that treeshelters do not substantially reduce the requirement for weed control and this aspect of management should never be neglected. Other early routine maintenance operations include retightening of ties, checking stakes, ensuring good ground contact at the base of the treeshelter and beating up. Maintenance is particularly important if the objects of management mean that the trees have been planted at a wide spacing, such as 3 m.

The importance of weeding around shelters is illustrated by the results in Figure 9. The mean height increment of the oak transplants was greatly increased by treeshelters, as would be expected, but in the unweeded shelters the height gain was only 652 mm compared with 1020 mm in the weeded shelters. In this experiment survival was not signifcantly affected by the shelters, but in both sheltered and unsheltered treatments it was significantly improved by killing the competing weeds. The methods of weed control tested included plastic mulch mats and a variety of herbicide

1. Deliver materials to rideside (separately or simultaneously depending on size of job).

2. Carry a reasonable manual load of stakes and walk along planting lines dropping one stake at each planting position. Pre-planting herbicide application will make this easier as well as providing maximum benefit to the newly-planted trees.

3. After dropping the last stake, turn and erect the stakes on the return journey, ensuring that the top of the stake will not project above the rim of the shelter where it may damage the stem. Complete the erection of stakes in this fashion.

4. Plant trees 4-5 cm from the stake on the leeward side with respect to the prevailing wind. This will reduce movement of the shelter. Trees are planted after stake erection to reduce root damage.

5. Carry a reasonable manual load of treeshelters and walk along planting lines dropping one shelter at each stake.

6. On the return journey attach each shelter to its stake and firm into the ground.

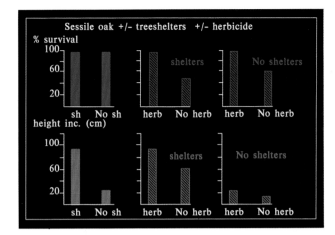

FIGURE 9 The relative influence of treeshelters and weed control on the early height growth and survival of sessile oak transplants.

regimes; there were no significant differences between the results of the different techniques. Although they offer a high degree of protection from mammals, treeshelters are not immune to damage, especially if less robust types are used. Intermittent inspections, particularly after strong winds and in early spring, are required to ensure that no further measures are necessary.

The final operation in the establishment period, while ensuring that the crop is not threatened by regrowth or unwanted regeneration, is to remove any stakes and wires that might damage the growing tree and dispose of the remaining fragments of plastic before they begin to cause a litter problem.

Financial considerations

There has been considerable debate over the issue of how large an area can economically be protected using treeshelters. The easiest answer comes from a direct comparison of material and labour costs for the provision of protection from animals by the different

Table 4		
	Site 1	**Site 2**
Tree species	Oak	Mixed broadleaves
Objects	Timber	Amenity
Plant spacing	2 m	3 m
Mammals present	Roe deer	Rabbits
Shape of planting site	Rectangular	Triangular
Dimensions	50 m × 100 m	200 m × 400 m × 450 m
Area	0.5 ha	4.0 ha
Fence length	300 m	1050 m
Cost per metre fence	3.62	2.10
Number of plants	1250	4400
Cost per shelter	86p	49.5p
Cost of fencing option	£1086	£2205
Cost of treeshelter option	£1075	£2178

options; no rule-of-thumb figure can be given as fencing costs depend greatly on the shape of the area and treeshelter costs depend on plant spacing.

While it is possible to formulate relationships between the cost of protection and the size and shape of areas, it must be emphasised that there is no substitute for a comparison of the actual costs involved in the various options available to the forest manager for each site. The calculations in Table 4, using 1988 values, illustrate ways in which this might be approached (figures are derived from work study comparisons and Insley, 1988).

The comparisons become more involved when one takes into account such factors as the shortened establishment period, the reduced cost of herbicide application, increased survival, maintenance and inspection costs, and the fact that if a fence is breached all trees are at risk whereas if a treeshelter is damaged only one tree is exposed.

It can be seen in Table 5 that although the comparison of initial costs seems to indicate that fencing is the cheaper option, when all the benefits accrued during the establishment period are taken into account treeshelters are seen, in this example, to be a better choice.

Plant spacing

With oak, beech and other species that exhibit considerable variation between individuals it is unwise to depend on a low initial stocking density if the production of quality timber is among the objects of management. Although 3 m spacing is permitted with broadleaved species in Forestry Commission grant schemes, this is a *maximum* distance between plants and should not be regarded as a general prescription for broadleaves.

An initial spacing of 2 m × 2 m is desirable on silvicultural grounds for most species if the aim is to produce valuable timber, with early tending oper-

Table 5 Broadleaves at 3 m spacing; roe deer present
Site roughly rectangular: 120 m × 280 m
Area = 3.36 ha; fence length = 800 m

Operation	Cost using fencing £ (1988)	Cost using treeshelter £ (1988)
Protection	2896	3179
Planting	853	853
Weeding (chemical)	100	90
Beat up	228	—*
Weeding 1	100	90
Weeding 2	100	90
Weeding 3	100	—†
Cleaning 1	150	150‡
Cleaning 2	150	—
Inspection	20	60§
Total cost to 3 years from planting	4697	4512

* Beating up not justified by typical number of losses
† Although early weeding is essential, annual herbicide applications can usually be halted a year or two sooner if treeshelters are used
‡ Cleaning costs will vary greatly according to site
§ Total during establishment period

ations directed towards achieving a minimum established stocking of 2000 evenly-spaced stems per net hectare. Such conditions provide side shelter, encourage upright growth and offer a wide choice of final crop trees. This is especially important for species such as oak and beech that exhibit poor apical dominance. This silvicultural requirement can be lessened if regrowth or regeneration of a suitable species is incorporated as a nurse or part of the final crop.

Treeshelters have surprisingly little influence on initial spacing requirements. The enhanced height growth is short lived, canopy closure being advanced by perhaps 1 or 2 years, and will have no long-term effect. Survival is generally improved with shelters but poorly-established crops with or without treeshelters are usually beaten up until a satisfactory stocking of at least 80% is achieved. It follows that the greatest contrast in stocking is likely to be a fully-stocked plantation in shelters and a conventionally-established area with 80% stocking.

If it is accepted that a stocking at the end of the establishment period of 2000 trees per hectare (i.e. 80% of 2500) is considered an acceptable result from 2 m planting, then this could be achieved by planting at 2.24 m in shelters. It should, however, be noted that this is the maximum effect that might be encountered and in most cases the differences in plant spacing requirements will be considerably less, particularly if wider initial spacings are used.

Natural regeneration

It is common to encounter dense regeneration during the summer, only to discover that by the following spring it has practically all disappeared. Ash may produce a carpet of seedlings at a density that, in patches, exceeds a million trees per hectare; within a year this has usually declined to a small fraction of the original number.

In most woodlands this disappearance can be attributed principally to browsing by mammals, which on many sites will include sheep. Treeshelters lend themselves ideally to the protection of natural regeneration, especially where this arises at irregular spacing over a period of several years.

Protection needs to be in place before winter, which in practical terms means by September with deciduous species. Treeshelters may be placed over seedlings at approximately regular spacing, aiming at a distance between plants of 3 m or less, or alternatively over individual seedlings in groups of 4 — 10 in patches of regeneration with a distance of 6 — 8 m between groups.

Treeshelters can also be used to exploit the regeneration that occurs in gaps in young plantations, accelerating height growth to help keep the crowns up with the main crop.

Birds and wood mice reduce the occurrence of regeneration by collecting large seeds as well as eating freshly emerging seedlings. Experience has shown that it is usually futile to try to use shelters over seed pressed into the ground but they can offer valuable protection once the cotyledons are apparent.

In situations where light intensities are high, the colour of treeshelters is unlikely to be of importance. However, on many sites where natural regeneration is occurring, irradiance is likely to be reduced by the presence of an overstorey and this may mean that the addition of a treeshelter leads to considerable light interception. The relevance of light intensity in shelters is discussed on page 18.

It can again be emphasised that treeshelters do not obviate the need for weeding; this is as true with 'wildings' as it is with planted trees.

PLATE 12   When treeshelters were used to protect browsed regeneration on Exmoor the seedlings reached the top of the 1.8 m shelters in 2 years. *(37234)*

Design of planting schemes

Although they might be viewed as an encouraging indication of tree planting, treeshelters in themselves are not, on the whole, an attractive sight in the country-side. It is therefore important to consider the landscape implications of schemes in which treeshelters are to be used. Treeshelters are an intrusive element in the rural scene because of their rigid geometry and smooth surfaces; the disharmony can be aggravated by an inappropriate choice of colour and ill-designed layout.

The original white shelters are among the most harsh and should generally be avoided, though they are useful in underplanting or other situations where light levels are already low (in full light they may increase plant stress by admitting more light and creat-ing higher temperatures). Although it might be supposed that green would blend well in the country-side some of the shades used for treeshelters are particularly unnatural and discretion should be exer-cised if green shelters are to be used. Pale brown is generally considered to be one of the most suitable colours for the majority of situations, although this will depend on the type of surrounding vegetation and dull olive-green or khaki may be better on some sites.

Large areas of uniform colour will always look unnatural, so where treeshelters are to be used on extensive areas the visual impact can be reduced by dividing up the site into several irregular sections and using different colours of shelter. Do not scatter differ-ent colours within a planting scheme as this creates an unpleasantly distracting clutter.

PLATE 13 White shelters are visually obtrusive, though they may be useful in very shaded positions. *(36244)*

PLATE 14 Different coloured shelters may be used to follow a changing pattern of vegetation.

The artificial appearance of treeshelters is unnecessarily emphasised by planting in a precise geometric grid. Unless mechanical weed control is employed (but see page 33) there is little need to follow rigidly straight lines. One of the main justifications for this in the past has been the difficulty in finding young plants in the year or two after planting; with treeshelters this is no problem. Despite what has been said above, it is important that the shelters are carefully erected and kept upright: a collection of plastic tubes leaning at various angles will create visual confusion as well as giving an impression of incompetence or neglect.

Most treeshelters will begin to decay after about 5 years. Flat-sided shelters will initially split along the creases at the corners, creating long strips of loose plastic. Other designs normally degrade into smaller pieces of material. The process is generally not rapid and ample opportunity is available for the residue to be collected if there is a risk of it causing a litter problem.

PLATE 15   Geometric planting patterns emphasise the presence of an unnatural element in the landscape.   *(36262)*

Appendix: The treeshelter microclimate

The main features that characterise the treeshelter microclimate are warmer temperatures, higher humidities, lack of air movement and reduced light intensity. In addition CO_2 concentrations, gas exchange rates and the spectral composition of light can be considerably different from those outside shelters. The complex way in which these factors interact in influencing plant development tends to obscure the contribution of each environmental component to the overall effect. Nevertheless it is clear that some parameters are strongly related to observations of plant growth and survival.

This is well illustrated by measurements taken on a bright summer's day (25.8.84) in Kent, when conditions outside treeshelters were compared with those in a shelter containing a small, newly-planted sessile oak transplant (*Quercus petraea* (Matt.) Lieb.) and one occupied by a larger, established tree with abundant foliage (Figure 10). Air temperature outside the treeshelters reached a maximum of about 28°C at 16.00 hours and then declined steadily during the late afternoon and evening. By comparison the relative humidity (r.h.) curve followed a more or less inverted course, reaching a minimum of 46% at the time of the highest temperature.

Maximum air temperatures in treeshelters were much higher than outside, reaching 38°C in the shelter containing a newly planted tree and 32°C in the shelter with the large tree. The r.h. was higher in both shelters falling to 66% in the shelter with the small tree while remaining high at all times in the shelter containing much transpiring foliage, remaining at 100% for most of the day but dropping briefly to a minimum of 8

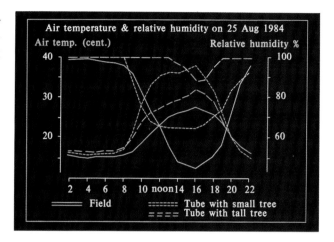

FIGURE 10   Temperature and relative humidity in a treeshelter containing a newly planted transplant, in a treeshelter containing an established transplant and outside the treeshelters (after Evans and Potter, 1985).

during the afternoon. The enclosed environment of the treeshelter is, in effect, acting as a 'solar still', with a high proportion of the moisture emitted by the tree and the soil condensing on the walls of the tube.

However, r.h. is not the most suitable indicator of the evaporative demand, or the 'drying power', of the air on trees in shelters because of its dependence on temperature. For such considerations vapour pressure deficit (V.P.D.) is a more appropriate measure and reflects more accurately the influence of atmospheric moisture on the physiological processes of a plant. For instance, an r.h. of 60% is equivalent at 20°C to a V.P.D. of 0.94 kPa

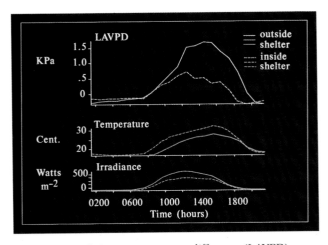

FIGURE 11 Leaf-air vapour pressure difference (LAVPD), temperature and irradiance inside and outside a treeshelter containing an established transplant.

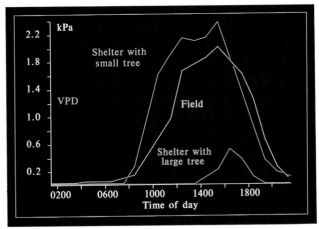

FIGURE 12 Vapour pressure deficit in a treeshelter containing a recently planted transplant, in a treeshelter containing an established transplant and outside the treeshelters.

and at 30°C to 1.70 kPa (this indicates that the drying power of air at the same r.h. is almost doubled with this increase in temperature). When considering transpiration rates, the evaporative demand on a plant leaf in any situation can be expressed in terms of leaf-to-air vapour pressure difference (LAVPD) which is the saturation vapour pressure at leaf temperature minus the vapour pressure of the air (it is assumed that air spaces within the leaf are occupied by saturated air).

LAVPDs for leaves of trees in the field and in a shelter are plotted against time in Figure 11, which also shows simultaneous curves for temperature and solar radiation. The data were collected on the same day in August and refer to the unsheltered tree and the tall tree in a shelter. It can be seen that, although still considerable, the difference between LAVPD for the two treatments was less than that for r.h.

The curves for temperature and total short-wave irradiance reveal interesting relationships with LAVPD. That of the tree in the tube peaked much earlier than the LAVPD of the unsheltered tree, at a point coinciding with the maximum incident radiation. The LAVPD of the field tree, on the other hand, reached a greater peak some 2 hours later at about the same time that air temperature maximises. The correlations of LAVPD in the two treatments with incident radiation and air temperature are shown in Figure 13.

Leaf temperature was not recorded for the smaller tree but the relative dryness of the air in each environment can be expressed in terms of V.P.D. Figure 12 shows that the V.P.D. of the air in the shelter containing the small tree was greater than that outside. This suggests that the risk of water stress in newly-planted trees may be as great or greater than that of unsheltered trees when high temperatures are experienced. However, provided the tree has been planted at an appropriate time of year (autumn or early spring) its foliage will normally be well-developed before summer tempera-

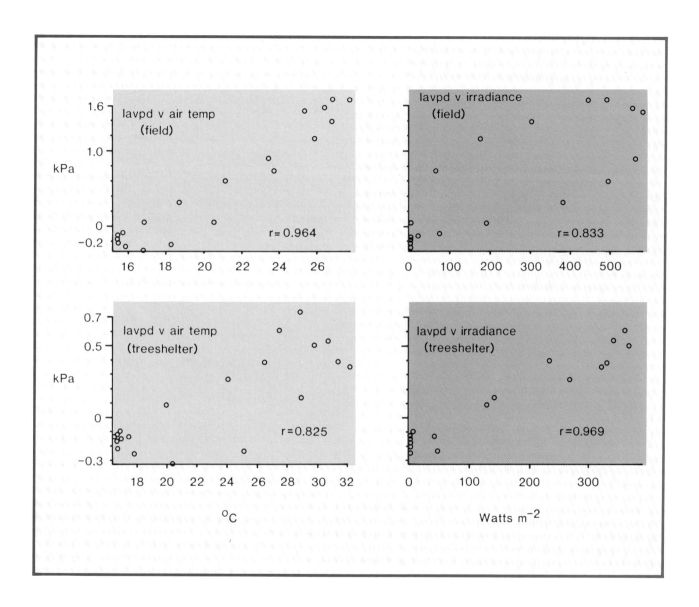

FIGURE 13 Correlations between LAVPD and air temperature, and LAVPD and irradiance, inside and outside a treeshelter containing an established transplant.

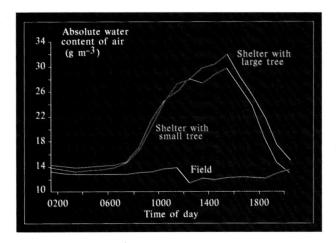

FIGURE 14 The absolute water content of air in a treeshelter containing a recently planted transplant, in a treeshelter containing an established transplant and outside the treeshelters.

tures are experienced and so conditions in the shelter will be approaching those in the shelter with the tall tree. It should also be remembered that the data refer to one relatively short-lived event: such exacting conditions are likely to be encountered on only a few occasions during a typical north-temperate summer.

If the values for absolute water content of the air in each of the three treatments are compared (Figure 14) it is seen that the field measurements remained more or less constant throughout the day. In the shelters the water content rose sharply during the morning, reaching a peak in the late afternoon (at about the same time as maximum temperature) and then declined rapidly. It is interesting, and perhaps somewhat surprising, to see that the two curves relating to trees with very different quantities of transpiring foliage followed very similar paths. This may be because transpiration was limited by a factor such as irradiance, which is the same in both shelters, or because the amounts of water emitted from the soil and re-evaporating from the walls of the shelter were much greater than that from the plant, thus masking the influence of transpiration, particularly during the morning when the treeshelter and the air it contains were first warmed by sunlight.

Air temperatures, both inside and out of treeshelters, began to decline about 3 hours after the maximum radiation was recorded, the temperature in the shelter being slightly lower than that outside once measurements of radiation fell to below about $10\,\mathrm{W\,m^{-2}}$. This may be explained largely by the rapid loss of heat by convection within a cooling treeshelter; the tube in which air movement was restricted by dense foliage cooled more slowly although the heat held by this mass of plant material could help maintain a higher temperature.

On relatively calm and sunny days most of the air movement in shelters is due to free convection caused by the expansion of air on heating as incident radiant energy is converted to heat and conducted through the plastic wall. During windy conditions turbulence is created in the shelter and, if the base is not sealed against the ground, throughflow may result in a rapid air exchange rate. Despite this, in even the most severe conditions this movement will be negligible compared with wind velocity outside shelters.

The relationship between wind and transpiration is complex. Air movement increases passive water loss (for instance, through the cuticle) and shortens the diffusive path length by increasing boundary layer turbulence while reducing surface temperature. Moderate wind speeds may increase water loss while higher speeds may close stomata through which water is lost and CO_2 gained. Strong winds can carry soil particles that abrade the cuticle and reduce the plant's control over water loss. Although the balance of these effects varies between species and may be influenced by other environmental conditions it is likely that changes described here help to explain the increased growth and survival observed for newly-planted trees protected by treeshelters. Lower LAVPDs and reduced wind movement might both be expected to increase photosynthetic CO_2 fixation relative to water loss.

The curves showing measurements of sunlight inside and outside treeshelters on a bright August day (part of Figure 12) follow very similar patterns ($r = 0.997$), those inside the tube remaining close to 68% of ambient. These measurements were made in a white polypropylene treeshelter, a type now little used. Light interception in currently popular models is likely to be 10 - 15% more than this. The response of plants in shelters to various proportions of light transmission is discussed in the section on treeshelter design.

Carbon dioxide concentrations in shelters occupied by established trees suggest that CO_2 fixation by photosynthesis is able to create and maintain measurable concentration gradients in the enclosed atmosphere (Figure 15). It appears that CO_2 originating from bacterial respiration in the soil is trapped in the lower part of the tube, an effect that is enhanced by sealing the shelter at the base by pressing it into the ground. As the gas moves up the tube by diffusion and convection it is rapidly consumed on contact with photosynthesising foliage resulting in a negative concentration gradient of CO_2 with height inside the shelter.

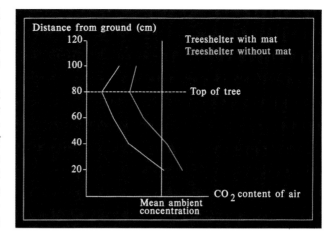

FIGURE 15   Carbon dioxide concentrations at different heights in treeshelters with and without plastic mats covering the soil surface.

Further reading

Treeshelters

EVANS, J. and POTTER, M. J. (1985). Manchons forestiers — un nouveau matériel pour la reprise des arbres. *Plasticulture* **68**, 7 — 20.

EVANS, J. and SHANKS, C. W. (1985). *Treeshelters.* Arboriculture Research Note 63/85/SILS.DOE Arboricultural Advisory and Information Service, Forestry Commission.

FREARSON, K. and WEISS, N. D. (1987). Improved growth rates with treeshelters. *Quarterly Journal of Forestry* **81**(3), 184 — 187.

POTTER, M. J. (1986). Major innovations mark the 1986 treeshelter scene. *Forestry and British Timber* **15**(10), 19.

POTTER, M. J. (1986). Treeshelters. In, *Report on Forest Research 1986,* 8 — 9. HMSO, London.

POTTER, M. J. (1987). Advances in treeshelter research and design. In, *Occasional Paper No.34,* ed. P. Savill, 1 — 4. Oxford Forestry Institute, Oxford.

POTTER, M. J. (1987). Shelter questions and answers. *Forestry and British Timber* **16**(10), 28 — 29.

POTTER, M. J. (1987). Vaekstror - sporgsmal og svar. *Skoven* **2/88**, 72 — 73.

POTTER, M. J. (1987). Treeshelters. In, *Report on Forest Research 1987,* 9 — 11. HMSO, London.

POTTER, M. J. (1988). Treeshelters improve survival and increase early growth rates. *Journal of Forestry* **86**(8), 39 — 41.

POTTER, M. J. (1989). Treeshelters: their influence on microclimate and tree establishment. Invited paper presented at *International Conference on Fast Growing and Nitrogen Fixing Trees,* Philips University Marburg (FRG), Oct. 1989.

RENDLE, E. L. (1985). The influence of tube shelters on microclimate and the growth of oak. *Proceedings of 6th Meeting of National Hardwoods Programme,* Oxford Forestry Institute, 8 — 16. National Hardwoods Programme, Oxford.

RENDLE, E. L. (1988). *Studies on the growth of young oak trees as affected by the environment, in particular photoperiod, temperature and also gibberellic acid application.* PhD Thesis, Wye College, University of London.

TULEY, G. (1980). Rural arboriculture. *Report on Forest Research 1980,* 15. HMSO, London.

TULEY, G. (1982). Tree shelters increase the early growth of broadleaved trees. In, Proceedings of a symposium entitled: *Broadleaves in Britain — future management and research,* eds D.C. Malcolm, J. Evans and P.N. Edwards, 176 — 182, University of Technology, Loughborough. Institute of Chartered Foresters, Edinburgh.

TULEY, G. (1983). Shelters improve the growth of young trees in the forest. *Quarterly Journal of Forestry* **77**(2), 77 — 87.

TULEY, G. (1984). Tree shelters take the greenhouse to the tree. *Forestry and British Timber* **13**(10), 17 — 19.

TULEY, G. (1985). The growth of young oak trees in shelters. *Forestry* **58**, 181 — 195.

Plants and microclimate

COLE, F. D. and DECKER, J. P. (1973). Relation of transpiration to atmospheric vapour pressure. *Journal of the Arizona Academy of Science* **8**, 74 — 75.

DAVIES, W. J., KOZLOWSKI, T. T. and PEREIRA, J. (1974). Effect of wind on transpiration and stomatal aperture in woody plants. In, *Mechanisms of regulation of plant growth,* eds B.L. Bieleski, A.R. Ferguson and M.M. Cresswell, 433 — 438. Bulletin 12, Royal Society of New Zealand.

DAY, W. (1985). Water vapour measurement and control. In, *Instrumentation for environmental physiology,* eds B. Marshall and F.I. Woodward, 59 — 78. Society for Experimental Biology Seminar Series 22. Cambridge University Press, Cambridge.

DIXON, M. and GRACE, J. (1984). Effect of wind on the transpiration of young trees. *Annals of Botany* **53**, 811 — 819.

FITTER, A. H. and HAY, R. K. M. (1987). *Environmental physiology of plants.* Academic Press, London.

FORD, M. A. and THORNE, G. N. (1974). Effects of atmospheric humidity on plant growth. *Annals of Botany* **38**, 441 — 452.

GARDNER, W. R. (1960). Dynamic aspects of water availability to plants. *Soil Science* **89**, 63 — 73.

GRACE, J. (1977). *Plant response to wind.* Academic Press, London.

GRACE, J. (1983). *Plant-atmosphere relationships.* Chapman and Hall, London.

HSAIO, T. C. (1973). Plant responses to water stress. *Annual Review of Plant Physiology* **24**, 519 — 570.

HSAIO, T. C., ACEVEDO, E., FERERES, E. and HENDERSON, D. W. (1976). Water stress, growth and osmotic adjustment. *Philosophical Transactions of the Royal Society B* **273**, 479 — 500.

HELMS, J. A. (1976). Factors affecting net photosynthesis. In, *Tree physiology and yield improvement,* eds M.C.R. Cannell and F.T. Last, 55 — 78. Academic Press, London.

HOLMGREN, P., JARVIS, P. J. and JARVIS, M. S. (1965). Resistance to CO_2 and water vapour transfer in leaves of different plant species. *Physiologica Plantarum* **18**, 557 — 573.

KOZLOWSKI, T. T. (1976). Water relations and tree improvement. In, *Tree physiology and yield improvement,* eds M.C.R. Cannell and F.T. Last, 307 — 327. Academic Press, London.

KOZLOWSKI, T. T. (1979). *Tree growth and environmental stresses.* University of Washington Press, Seattle.

KRAMER, P. J. (1969). *Plant and soil water relationships.* McGraw-Hill, New York.

KRAMER, P. J. (1983). *Water relations of plants.* Academic Press, London.

LARCHER, W. (1980). *Physiological plant ecology,* 2nd edition. Springer-Verlag, Berlin.

LARSON, M. M. (1980). Effects of atmospheric humidity and zonal soil water stress on initial growth of planted northern red oak seedlings. *Canadian Journal of Forest Research* **10**, 549 — 554.

LAVENDER, D. P. (1980). Effects of the environment upon the shoot growth of woody plants. In, *The control of shoot growth of trees. Proceedings of joint workshop of IUFRO working parties on xylem and shoot growth physiology,* ed. C.H.A. Little, 76 — 106. IUFRO, Corvallis, Oregon.

LEVITT, J. (1980). *Responses of plants to environmental stress.* Academic Press, London.

LONGMAN, K. A. and COUTTS, M. P. (1974). Physiology of the oak tree. In, *The British oak; its history and natural history,* eds M.G. Morris and F.H. Perring, 194 — 221. Classey, Faringdon.

MILBURN, J. A. (1979). *Water flow in plants.* Longman, London.

PEREIRA, J. S. and KOZLOWSKI, T. T. (1977). Influence of light intensity, temperature and leaf area on stomatal aperture and water potential of woody plants. *Canadian Journal of Forest Research* **7**, 145 — 153.

TIMMIS, R. (1980). Stress resistance and quality criteria for tree seedlings; analysis, measurement and use. *New Zealand Journal of Forest Science* **10**(1), 21 — 53.

VAN WIJK, W. F. (1966). *Physics of plant environment.* North Holland Publishing Company, Amsterdam.

Protection from mammals

DAVIES, H. L. and TAYLOR, C. M. A. (1988). Protection of young trees in agroforestry in the UK. In, *Proceedings of Research Meeting no. 1.* British Grassland Society, Maidenhead.

DAVIES, R. J. and PEPPER, H. W. (1989). The influence of small plastic guards, treeshelters and weed control on damage to young broadleaved trees by field voles *(Microtis agrestis). Journal of Environmental Management* **28**, 117 — 125.

PEPPER, H. W. (1978). *Netlon tree guards.* Forestry Commission Research Information Note 41/78/WILD. Forestry Commission, Edinburgh.

PEPPER, H. W., ROWE, J. J. and TEE, L. A. (1985). *Individual tree protection.* Arboricultural Leaflet 10. HMSO, London.

PEPPER, H. W. and TEE, L. A. (1986). *Forest fencing.* Forestry Commission Leaflet 87. HMSO, London.

POTTER, C. J. and TAYLOR, C. M. A. (1989). Agroforestry. In, *Report on Forest Research 1989,* 14. HMSO, London.

Silviculture

ANON. (1989). *Forest landscape design guidelines.* Forestry Commission, Edinburgh.

DAVIES, R. J. (1987). *Trees and weeds — weed control for successful tree establishment.* Forestry Commission Handbook 2. HMSO, London.

EVANS, J. (1984). *Silviculture of broadleaved woodland.* Forestry Commission Bulletin 62. HMSO, London.

EVANS, J. (1988). *Natural regeneration of broadleaves.* Forestry Commission Bulletin 78. HMSO, London.

HIBBERD, B. G. (ed.) (1988). *Farm woodland practice.* Forestry Commission Handbook 3. HMSO, London.

HIBBERD, B. G. (ed.) (1991). *Forestry practice,* 11th edn. Forestry Commission Handbook 6. HMSO, London.

INSLEY, H. (ed.) (1988). *Farm woodland planning.* Forestry Commission Bulletin 80. HMSO, London.

MIEGROET, M. van, VERGEGGHE, J. F. and LUST, N. (1981). Trends of development in the early stages of mixed natural regenerations of ash and sycamore. *Sylva Gandavensis* **48**, 1 - 29.

Printed in the United Kingdom for HMSO
Dd 291292 C60 4/91